mobile working

how businesses can improve
efficiency and productivity

consultant editor: Marc Beishon
sub-editor: Lesley Malachowski
production manager: Lisa Robertson
design: Halo Design
commercial director: Ed Hicks
publishing director: Tom Nash
chief operating officer: Andrew Main Wilson
chairman: Miles Templeman

Published for the Institute of Directors
and Vodafone UK by Director Publications Ltd
116 Pall Mall London SW1Y 5ED
Ⓣ 020 7766 8950 Ⓦ www.iod.com

 **BlackBerry**.

vodafone.co.uk/blackberry

Get email on your phone.
And phone people about their emails.

Introducing the new BlackBerry 7100v.™ It's a phone that also emails. No plugging in.
No logging on. No tearing your hair out. Just turn it on and there's your inbox.
Unlike other phones it has a unique keypad, so messages are even quicker to type.
Tough enough for everday use, it really does the business. And with its sleek lines,
it looks it, too. But best of all, as soon as you get the message, you can make the call.
To find out more visit your local Vodafone Store or call 0800 587 8057.

The email phone. From Vodafone.

CONTENTS

Peter Judge, Philip Hunter, Sally Flood, Sandra Vogel, Marc Ambasna-Jones, Steve Gold and Malcolm Wheatley are independent business and technology writers.

a great opportunity

Mike O'Brien MP, Minister of State for Energy and E-Commerce

Mobile technology has changed the ways we live and work. But its real potential has not yet been achieved. Harnessing technology is vital for businesses – including the smallest businesses – who want to perform better. The 2004 International Benchmarking Study, recently published by DTI, shows that there is an undeniable link between effective use of Information and Communication Technology (ICT) and productivity. Among the new trends emerging this year are that businesses in the UK and elsewhere are increasingly selective in their application of ICT, and are much more astute in measuring its benefits.

I welcome the initiative taken by the IoD and Vodafone to produce a practical guide to help businesses choose and use mobile technologies that can enable them to work better and smarter. It makes sense to develop a clear and flexible strategy on mobile working and to consider the business benefits your organisation can expect to gain from mobile solutions.

Within 20 years mobile and wireless have become rapidly maturing and pervasive technologies. 3G products and services are now available, with the potential to transform how we access data and information. The government is committed to ensuring that UK businesses can harness the power of these technologies to support communications, commerce and innovation.

There is a great opportunity for businesses of all sizes to boost their performance (such as by saving on time or costs) through clever deployment of new, mobile ways of working. This publication, containing a mix of information, advice and case studies, is a good place from which to start that process.

power brings responsibility

**Miles Templeman, Director General
Institute of Directors**

A defining technology of the 21st century will be 'electronic mobility'. The 19th and 20th centuries gave us increasing 'physical mobility' through the ship, the train, the car and the aircraft. Those new freedoms transformed business and personal life, as well as facilitating very large-scale economic development. Electronic mobility will give us the complementary opportunity of being able to work (or play) as we choose, at any time and anywhere.

The growing capabilities of the wireless technologies outlined in this guide, together with major advances such as micro-fuel cells for powering mobile devices, will lead to there being no need to be physically tethered to communications or worried about batteries running down, whether in the office, at home, or on the move.

Such technical power represents a double-edged sword. Used well it can facilitate more fulfilling and productive business and personal lives. It offers new scope for improving customer service and responsiveness and many new opportunities to gain competitive advantage. In ten years' time we may well look back and wonder how we managed without extensive mobile working.

But used badly, it could be a nightmare of poor practice, increased stress, and uncontrolled costs. In particular, failing to follow good practice on security – whether physical, in terms of mobile devices themselves, or electronic, through Virtual Private Networks and encryption – could quite possibly snatch business defeat from the jaws of victory.

This Director's Guide is timely, for mobile operators and service providers are starting to bring genuine business applications, and not simply technology, to the market. These packaged applications, and the measurable business benefits that they bring, are particularly relevant for small and medium sized businesses.

The guide outlines the new possibilities opened up by the tools of mobile working. It explains, in straightforward terms, the range of mobile communications options and gives clear guidance on taking the critical first steps in establishing good corporate policies. Not least, it details how to stay on the right side of the complexities of health and safety and data protection law. Of particular importance is the recommendation to carefully review existing business practices and processes, as these can often be simplified and transformed to extract yet more cost savings and service improvements. I commend this guide to you.

a natural way of doing business

Bill Morrow, CEO, Vodafone UK

In today's business environment, there are few excuses for a slow response to enquiries, neglected opportunities or missed deadlines. Customers and suppliers expect businesses to work smartly and have the basic measures in place to deliver good customer service – whatever the size of company. The consequences of not achieving this will negatively affect company reputation and ultimately give your competitors the upper hand.

Since the first mobile phone call was made, 30 years ago, our daily life has changed quite radically. Today, mobile capabilities have expanded beyond the initial function for voice communication, to downloading games and music for consumers, and to accessing email, office information and using a wide variety of applications for business. In the same way that technology, such as the Internet and email, plays a ubiquitous role in our daily work routine, mobile technology is becoming a natural part of how we do business.

Although technology has helped to increase productivity and efficiency, companies still suffer pressures from competition, regulation and, critically, time. Customers expect services to be available 24/7, or simply to be more 'available' during working hours. Mobile technology can help satisfy this requirement, by improving communication with customers, colleagues and suppliers. This need not be expensive or complex; it can be as simple as texting a colleague out of the office, or responding to a customer enquiry out of traditional working hours. Such practices help reduce overheads, save time and are cost-effective.

In addition to tangible benefits, there are also other advantages of implementing mobile solutions within your business. For example, improving mobile working or enabling flexible working practices can have a fundamental effect on the attractiveness of a company. Becoming more flexible can help reduce staff turnover and create a happier workforce. The Work Foundation reported that 47 per cent of employees seek flexibility in their jobs. For example, among 18-24 year-olds, 80 per cent said they would be more motivated if they had access to work-life balance schemes.

Vodafone UK is in an advantageous position where we are able to implement, and see the positive effects of, the latest mobile technology in our own workplace. Consequently, it recognises the influence that its products and services have on the UK working environment. It believes that nearly all businesses can be aided by the move to become 'mobile'.

A Vodafone survey recently found that over 80 per cent of business professionals are now equipped for mobile working, with 42 per cent using mobile data technologies, such as Wi-Fi, mobile data cards and BlackBerry™ devices. It is not surprising that Gartner, the industry analyst, estimates that mobile e-mail is one of the most important innovations to British business today and will improve mobile worker productivity by up to 10 per cent by 2008.

The following chapters will identify both simple and advanced ways of using mobile technology. Before implementing any technology, it is critical to consider your strategy. Among the issues you should consider when developing a strategy are: what you need, who should use it, and how you can measure the success of any deployment.

A mobile solution can be one of the building blocks to ensure your company runs effectively. This guide should help to ensure how you choose the best devices and price plans for your company without distracting you from your primary objective – running your business.

mobile trends

Mobile phones were first developed 30 years ago. Today, there are nearly a billion mobile phone users around the world. Peter Judge, business and technology writer, gives an overview of the current picture

You may think you already know the benefits of mobile working: many workers now have mobile phones, which have increased their productivity and allowed them to be in contact with whoever they choose.

But mobile working is not standing still. In the next few years there will be big changes in the way we use mobility to maximise our working days. There are many ways to connect while on the move, and more of us will be mobile by default, only sitting at a desk when it suits us, and otherwise working wherever we are.

"Remote working today is no poor relation," says Tim Hubbard, director of next generation networks (NGN) technical marketing at Nortel. "It no longer entails expensive low speed dial-up solutions and it is no longer restricted by the capabilities of your home phone and laptop."

EXECUTIVE SUMMARY

☐ mobile working makes us all more productive, linking us to co-workers and IT systems wherever we are

☐ mobile tools will help employers to bring about about flexible working, respond to demographic changes such as longer journeys to work, and keep up with competitors

☐ devices such as smartphones, handheld computers and laptops are improving. They are bringing down the cost of communications and becoming so reliable that mobile working will be the norm

As well as phones, there are laptops and PDAs (personal digital assistants), and mobile devices for blue-collar workers. And the networks that connect them are developing, offering faster speeds and more reliable services.

FACTS AND FIGURES

- ☐ fifty five per cent of managers will work outside the office at some point this year (Nortel)
- ☐ UK business lost the equivalent of $8bn in 2004 from 'dead time' travelling (YouGov)
- ☐ there are 20 million remote workers in the US and 10 million in Europe (ITAC)
- ☐ laptop sales will exceed desktops in 2005 (Current Analysis)

More importantly, the demand is there. Already, much of the workforce spends some time working outside the office, and various factors – from the forces of global competition to the more flexible lives we are leading – are pushing us further in that direction.

why are we mobile?

"A recent survey of more than 1,200 mid-level and higher managers found that 55 per cent of their corporate workforce works from outside the office, either at home or on the road, at sometime during the year," says Nortel's Tim Hubbard.

But why is this trend taking place? One simple reason is that we're working more than we used to. Global competition has reinforced the UK's infamous 'long hours culture', with executives often required to be available '24/7' to respond to demands from an international office or an overseas client.

Another reason is the desire to achieve a better work-life balance. Mobile working's biggest 'soft' benefit is that it gives workers the ability to balance their home and work life, for instance, enabling parents to work at home and see more of their children. Recent research from the Institute of Directors reveals that 56 per cent of the labour force worked flexible hours in 1999, but by the end of 2003 the figure had risen to 63 per cent. "Typically, working flexibly might mean a mother starting work early so she can pick up her child from school, giving her more time to teach the youngster to cook or watch TV together," says Richard Wilson, head of business policy at the IoD.

There are inevitably issues around how to control home-working so that neither work efficiency nor quality of personal life are disrupted. But again,

A DRAMATIC CUT IN COSTS

By selecting the right mobile technology tools, executives on the move can experience all the benefits of being back at the office and make significant savings on cost.

While staying in Abu Dhabi, Tim Hubbard, director of next generation networks (NGN) technical marketing at Nortel, kept in touch with business contacts across the world by using the hotel's Ethernet service, and saved a fortune. "I needed to be responsive and complete actions resulting from business meetings that day," he says.

"Despite being almost 4,000 miles away, I worked in exactly the same way as if I was sitting at my desk in Maidenhead, England," he says. Hubbard plugged his laptop into the hotel Ethernet LAN and established a secure high-speed connection to Nortel via the Internet, and used a multimedia client on his laptop. "I could make and receive telephone and video calls using the multimedia client. Everyone I called, and those people who called me, just assumed I was sitting at my desk," he says. "I also responded to new emails and voicemails I'd received during the day, at the same time and over the same connection."

The hotel's Ethernet service costs £12. "I worked out that if I'd used the telephone line in my room to access my email and my mobile to make my telephone calls, it would have cost me close to £1,000 (approx 1,600 Euros)." But it isn't just savings: using a multimedia tool allowed Hubbard to put people on hold, transfer calls and take part in conference calls.

technology is providing answers. Simple mobile phone services such as voicemail, message taking and call redirection allow home-based workers to manage their availability. In future, the ability of workers to screen and filter calls, emails and other communications will be enhanced.

For some people spending part of the working week at home is a way to save the hours spent travelling. For others, the opportunity to work while travelling makes the best use of a situation, turning dead time into productive time.

The benefits of flexible working are so obvious that more employers are offering it but, increasingly, this option is becoming a right, not a privilege. European legislation (enshrined in the UK's Employment Act 2002) gives many employees – specifically those with young or disabled children – the right to request flexible working, and this includes the opportunity to work at home, where the job is appropriate.

The step from being based in a fixed location to becoming a mobile worker is not a big one. It means using technology you can carry (or travel with), and a network connection that works outside the office or home.

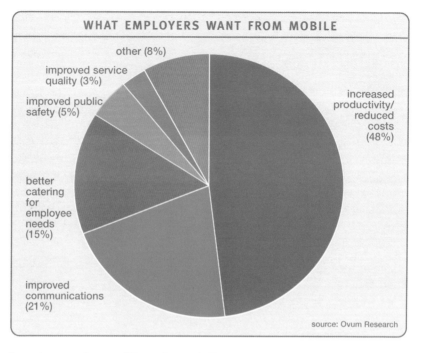

WHAT EMPLOYERS WANT FROM MOBILE

other (8%)

improved service quality (3%)

improved public safety (5%)

increased productivity/ reduced costs (48%)

better catering for employee needs (15%)

improved communications (21%)

source: Ovum Research

business benefits of mobile

The benefits of mobile working are so obvious that studies rarely enumerate them. Being in touch with colleagues all the time makes work more efficient and productive. If you get a business call while on the train, or waiting at an airport, you can cut out wasteful 'telephone tag' and move the project on to the next stage without delay. It might be a short call to clarify a simple point, but without it, the job would have to wait for a day or more.

The provision of mobile phones by companies is still low, despite the apparent benefits. But raw statistics on this can be deceptive. Mobile phones are now so cheap that most people have one, and many employees will use their own mobile phones for business calls. Typically, the cost of these is then reimbursed by their company via a routine claim for business expenses.

If you can also send an email or access a client record, then you have moved to the next level: data access. Instead of being able to merely talk and pass on jobs, you can actually do business wherever you are.

There are other gains: field sales and support staff can communicate easily with headquarters, access vital information on customers and, literally, cover more ground. And if office staff are mobile, there are fewer people in the office, leading to overall space savings and lower costs.

Given all these benefits, you would expect mobile working to be taking off, and it is. IT managers at 82 per cent of companies provide (or plan to provide) mobile access to senior management, according to Rhetorik Research. The figures are 55 per cent for the sales force, 40 per cent for service engineers and 22 per cent for logistics/delivery personnel.

According to surveys carried out by the International Telework Association and Council (ITAC), there are 28 million remote workers the US, and around 20 million in Europe. And this may be the tip of the iceberg: tacit mobile working is rife, even in organisations that haven't approved it officially. Even so, the potential is still not being fully exploited. A recent YouGov survey said 'dead time' is costing British businesses almost £8bn a year, with much of it being lost to travel.

what we carry and how it connects us

The first cellular phone call ever made was by Dr Martin Cooper of Motorola from a street in Manhatten in 1973. He is reputed to have made it to a rival development team at AT&T saying "mine's working, how about yours!". More certain is that, since then, the phone has been the core mobile communications tool. But this is changing. The big growth area now will not be in voice calls, but in the transfer of data, which includes email and Internet access. Data-handling mobile devices are coming into their own, such as the BlackBerry™ mobile email device, the laptop and the handheld computer or PDA.

The most basic mobile phones now synchronise contacts, calendar and email access with the most usual office software, and 'smartphones' can handle real-time email and link with business applications and the Internet.

At the same time, PDAs have moved on from the early devices. In today's mobile market, they come in various guises and offer a wide array of services – phone, email, Internet and other business applications.

13

Clearly, these technologies are overlapping in their offerings. Smartphones (designed originally for voice communications) and PDAs (built for data) are fighting for the pockets of the world's business people (see chapter 10).

Meanwhile, most executives prefer to have a laptop to travel with. According to Current Analysis, sales of laptops exceeded those of desktops for one week in May 2004, and are expected to out sell desktops over the whole year in 2005.

Mobile devices are by no means confined to executives. Other mobile workers such as delivery drivers and field engineers are increasingly using bespoke terminals designed for reliability and simplicity. Their price is comparatively high, but they have a very well-defined return on investment.

Indeed, mobile applications don't necessarily require any human interaction, with devices now being used to communicate data from one machine to another. Vending machines, for example, can automatically communicate their stock levels to the appropriate remote supplier, enabling efficient restocking.

So how are these devices connecting? Outside the office, there are three main network types:

- ☐ mobile network (GPRS and 3G), which has broad coverage and a lower data rate

- ☐ Wi-Fi hotspots, which have fast data rates but are more rare

- ☐ broadband connectivity at home

These network types can increasingly be accessed via a single laptop. Advances in connectivity are covered in Chapter 10.

mobile working is here to stay

The message to business is clear: the trend towards flexible working practices is strong and irreversible – and for very good business and lifestyle reasons. The key for businesses is to understand this trend, and to protect their future competitiveness by blending the innovative and evolving technologies with new ways of working.

MOBILE WORKING TRENDS

☐ **more hours on the road**
Professionals are spending an increasing proportion of their time outside the office – from 25% of working hours two years ago, to an anticipated 42% in two years' time.

☐ **no such thing as a typical working day**
Work day patterns are becoming increasingly fragmented as a result of globalisation.

☐ **virtual workplace relationships common**
Business people increasingly work in virtual teams across geographies.

☐ **communication is the main out-of-office activity**
The most common work performed outside the office is communication with colleagues and business contacts, whether in face-to-face meetings, by phone or via email.

☐ **productivity is high**
Business professionals have been quick to embrace the shift towards greater mobility, with the majority feeling as or more productive working outside the office as within.

☐ **mobile working delivers significant business benefits**
The majority of professionals see mobile working and wireless technology delivering significant competitive advantage.

☐ **wireless technology increasingly pervasive**
A majority of professionals own a laptop and wireless hotspot usage is a growing trend.

☐ **control over professional and personal lives**
Three-quarters of professionals believe mobile working allows them greater control over their professional lives and 60% perceive benefits in managing their personal lives.

☐ **barriers to mobile working**
Security concerns and cost top the list of reasons companies cite for not encouraging more mobile working.

☐ **EU to boost mobile working**
The majority of respondents see EU enlargement as a future driver of mobile working.

Source: Destination Wireless survey, Economist Intelligence Unit for Intel.

Now your attachments can fly around Europe just like you

Slot the Vodafone Mobile Connect 3G/GPRS data card into your laptop when you're travelling on business and get high-speed connection up to seven times faster than dial up. So you can download email attachments, browse the internet and get company files in a hurry when you're on the move. Accessible in over 250 European cities, the Vodafone 3G network has wider global coverage than any other 3G network – and it's growing all the time. Stop flying around for a minute and call 0800 587 8057 or visit your local Vodafone Store.

Our fast 3G data card makes mobile working work in over 250 European cities

towards a mobile strategy

> Keep your cool when confronted by the vast array of mobile options and you'll reap real benefits, says Philip Hunter, technology and business writer

While many businesses have mobiles, few have a coherent mobile strategy. Often this is because they are lulled into inaction by the bewildering range of device types and service packages. For mobile data it can also be hard to choose between the different network types, notably Wi-Fi, GPRS and 3G.

EXECUTIVE SUMMARY

- ☐ flexibility should be the watch word when developing a mobile strategy
- ☐ categorising workers according to need is a critical first step
- ☐ mobile operators are going the extra mile to cater for SMEs

While companies may be tempted to wait for the current confusion in the mobile market to subside, and for prices of devices and calls to fall, such logic is false, since your competitors will meanwhile exploit existing technology to boost productivity and improve service to customers. In any case, given that most firms make at least some use of mobile communications, a well-considered strategy should reduce costs and improve efficiency straightaway.

The problems of an ad hoc mobile roll-out are well-documented, including excessive costs and loss of control over data with attendant risks of theft of intellectual property and breaches of privacy. This has been exacerbated by the explosive growth of Wi-Fi hot spots, which many employees are making liberal use of and claiming on expenses.

ELIMINATING DEAD TIME

Property Intelligence is the leading provider of commercial property information in the UK. The company, which is part of the US-based CoStar group, offers a database of information containing details on over 400,000 commercial buildings (office, industrial, leisure and retail). This includes addresses, names of owners and occupiers, details on deals done, space availability, ratings, requirements, high resolution photographs, auctions and other information such as town reports. These are of great value to the commercial property professional.

A number of Property Intelligence's staff spend a lot of time on the road, either conducting product demonstrations at customers' premises or researching property data to upload onto the company system. Prior to using the latest mobile services, they were often unable to respond to customer or internal emails in a timely manner.

Matthew Hopkinson, operations director for Property Intelligence, explains: "Our staff tend to work in the field, some with a home office as their only base, so it was difficult for them to monitor correspondence throughout the day. We decided to introduce BlackBerrys™ to give our sales and management teams the necessary communication tools to maximise their performance."

Property Intelligence's customers are now able to correspond with their account manager throughout the day, meaning requests can often be dealt with immediately. In addition, when the management team previously travelled to CoStar's headquarters in Washington DC keeping in contact was difficult. However, the BlackBerry™ device used by the company is tri-band, which facilitates seamless roaming to the US. Staff are also able to use the service in any country in the world that has a GPRS roaming agreement with Vodafone UK.

Hopkinson adds: "BlackBerry™ is a considerable benefit for me when I'm travelling. The sheer simplicity of it is tremendous. Knowing that I'll be alerted to any new messages is extremely valuable and turns previously 'dead time', such as travelling in cabs or waiting for baggage, into productive worktime."

After a year's experience of BlackBerry™, Property Intelligence invested in 10 Vodafone Mobile Connect 3G/GPRS data cards for its field sales and management teams.

These enable staff to demonstrate the company's web product live over a 3G connection, regardless of the premises they are in. It has also allowed more meetings to be held away from the office since heavy documents, such as PowerPoint presentations, can now be downloaded without the need for a local network connection. "We recently acquired a company in Glasgow," says Hopkinson. "During the final negotiations the local network failed. Using a datacard we were able to connect to the Internet and send important legal documents to lawyers in order to close the deal."

Investing in these mobile tools has directly impacted on Property Intelligence's sales growth. "Since we deployed BlackBerry™ and Vodafone Mobile Connect 3G/GPRS data cards, our sales force is selling more than ever before," says Hopkinson. "I would estimate that I'm now working about 20 per cent more effectively than before."

Although a mobile strategy cannot anticipate the unexpected, if it's sufficiently flexible and adaptable it will at least encourage the emergence of new applications or services rather than stand in their way. Other than flexibility, any mobile strategy should possess the following features:

- ☐ accessibility of data

- ☐ functionality of devices in the field

- ☐ manageability

- ☐ total cost of ownership (TCO)

Each of these attributes needs to be considered in the context of mobile workers and their requirements.

In the case of using mobiles for calls this is more straightforward, as it mainly involves identifying the most cost-effective tariff package. On this front, usage patterns can help identify the best solution. For example, if the bulk of mobile traffic is internal then a package offering free calls to other employees and back to the office would be attractive, provided that the ongoing cost is reasonable.

However, in most cases the picture is broadened by data – such as access to email and the Internet – whose requirements should be considered as part of an overall package. Fortunately, mobile operators are well-geared to SMEs and offer some good packages, providing integrated voice and data services, options that enable costs to be contained and, crucially, with single bills.

categorising workers and their needs

This begs the question of what sort of devices mobile workers should be given. In some cases separate devices for voice and data will be best, for example, a laptop and standard phone. In other cases, particularly where the level of voice traffic is low and there is no need to enter vast amounts of text, the best choice might be a combined device. Such devices are no longer as unwieldy as before. The new BlackBerry™ 7100v from Vodafone, for example, is compact and stylish and offers combined access to voice and key data services such as email, calendar and basic office applications. This incorporates a neat QWERTY keyboard for replying to emails.

PLANNING A MOBILE WORKING CAMPAIGN

- [ ] examine your business applications: could your workers be more productive if they could access these tools at home or on the road?

- [ ] look at mobile email solutions for your staff, and mobile calendar/contacts support

- [ ] empower your 'blue-collar' staff with mobile devices. If they have to call in to the office for paperwork, you are losing productivity

- [ ] review the type and cost of your mobile contracts: consider upgrading so as to issue mobile phones to more staff

- [ ] arrange a security policy for mobile data

- [ ] consider if your company should have a formal programme for flexible working

The process of matching devices to tasks is best done by categorising mobile workers according to need. This is a vital aspect of a mobile strategy, involving constant amendment as both requirements and the available technology evolve. However, broadly speaking, there are five categories of mobile worker:

- [ ] those making occasional trips outside the office, who only need access to voice services. Basic voice mobile should suffice

- [ ] staff who travel frequently and require voice, but also limited data access (mostly email). A lightweight PDA or smartphone would be a good choice

- [ ] workers who collect extensive data in the field – such as reading utility meters – who only need limited access to central data. Such staff may be served best by robust dedicated data devices, perhaps with specialised reporting and aggregation software

- [ ] knowledge and power workers, such as field service engineers, who require extensive access to central databases. This type of worker may need a laptop, or perhaps an intermediate palmtop, that has a QWERTY keyboard with good functions for navigating through databases

- [ ] heavy duty mobile workers who generate large documents in the field or require display capabilities for presentations, eg. salespeople. Laptops (with data cards) are needed, along with separate mobiles for voice and perhaps email alerting.

Work patterns need to be characterised in order to assign mobile workers to the correct category. This process may be time-consuming, but the effort is worth it, for it will not just identify the correct choice of device, but also indicate what information and services will need to be made available from the central site.

This may reveal the need to integrate databases and core business applications with the mobile network. For SMEs lacking sufficient inhouse development resources this can be a deterrent. However, there is a range of solutions that need not be expensive or complex.

For most firms, the primary focus of their mobile strategy is staff in the field. However, for many, there is another dimension that will figure increasingly over the next few years – fixed equipment. By embedding SIM cards into equipment, SMS alerts can be sent to a service centre requesting an engineer's visit when a fault occurs. Often it is not convenient or cost-effective to connect such equipment to a fixed telephone line, especially when the requirement for such alerts is only occasional. This again requires central integration, and would form part of an overall field management system. The ability to generate alerts or messages automatically will also be a feature of mobile wireless devices, either carried by people or installed in vehicles. So, this possibility will also need to be catered for.

There is potential overlap here with location-based services (LBS). For example, an engineer's mobile, or vehicle, could report regularly on its position with the help of LBS, making it easier to track progress and plan visits from a central location. LBS-equipped devices can calculate a target's position to within a few metres by comparing how long signals take to reach them from three or more different nearby mobile phone masts, or from satellites if the Global Positioning System (GPS) is used instead. LBS is being adopted by logistics companies, which are using it to trace the precise location of customer orders. Other businesses would be wise to track such emerging technologies, which have potential applications in mobile communications.

seeing the big picture

Unlike IT or traditional telephony, mobile implementation has often been led by small business groups or even individual employees acting independently.

There has been little control over either capital or operating costs. Usage is often billed as an expense, bypassing central accounting, and sometimes the capital costs are absorbed in distributed departmental budgets. Costs spiral and security of valuable or sensitive data can be compromised.

The solution is to bring mobility directly under control of the IT director or, for smaller firms, the finance director. Their key issue is to consider the company's overall communications usage – including how your staff interact with each other and with customers and suppliers. It is important to establish total communications spend – with a full breakdown of how and where the costs are incurred, including fixed line telecom costs and IT expenditure, as well as the costs of mobile calls and email or Internet usage.

who can help?

Help may be needed to develop the best mobile strategy and determine the optimum billing plan, and this can be obtained from three sources: network operators, independent consultants, or providers of complete mobility solutions including devices as well as planning. All have their pros and cons: operators might be the cheapest, but can't be impartial when it comes to the network. Consultancies should be independent but are often too expensive for smaller companies. Solution providers could provide the right combination of price and advice, but care needs to be taken in choosing the right one. Points to consider include the cost and flexibility of tariffs or bill plans. The aim should be to control costs and also justify the investment in business terms, requiring an understanding of where and why mobile devices are being used. Training for your own staff may also be needed, not just in mastering the technology, but also in using it cost-effectively.

Given all these variables the ideal mobile strategy can be tough to nail down. Inevitably compromises will have to be made between cost and flexibility, as well as between accessibility and security. Yet, in spite of these issues, it's clear that in a fast-moving field, excessive caution is likely to prevent important business opportunities from being seized.

improving customer relations

Utilising CRM in the field can vastly improve the competitiveness of smaller companies, says Sally Flood, business and technology writer

There are some businesses that offer such great customer service you can't imagine going anywhere else. What do these successful businesses have in common? They know that every interaction with a customer is a chance to better understand, and serve, that customer. And, achieving that understanding is the job of customer relationship management (CRM).

EXECUTIVE SUMMARY

☐ the cost of CRM products for SMEs range from £150 to many thousands

☐ CRM vendors will host software for smaller business customers that don't have the resources or expertise to roll out software internally

☐ having a clear rationale for using CRM is essential: it's not the be all and end all of customer service

In the context of mobile working, CRM at its simplest is about being readily available to customers, perhaps 24/7, and responding promptly to their enquiries while on the move. At the very least, therefore, it requires access to mobile phone calls. In many cases email on the move is also a 'must'. And, it will often also require remote access to customer information held on company databases.

At the next level of sophistication comes CRM software that helps companies reduce costs by automating key sales and customer service processes. CRM also promises to improve customer acquisition and retention by pulling together all the information a business holds on its customers, and using it to provide a more personalised and responsive service. So when Amazon recommends a book you might like, or

BOOSTING EFFICIENCY

Ikon, one of the UK's leading suppliers of office equipment, employs 300 field service engineers to keep the company's photocopiers, printers and fax machines up and running.

Each technician is responsible for a specific part of the country and might only return to Ikon's head office once a month. Previously, engineers were notified of new jobs by pager and would phone Ikon's call centre when they were finished. The engineer also completed a three-ply FSR (Field Service Report) to record details of maintenance visits. This was sent back to head office by post or fax.

"The problem was that providing phones and pagers was expensive, and forms were often lost or illegible," explains national customer service director Marco Pezzani. "So in 2002, we began looking for a mobile solution that would improve matters."

Ikon now uses a mobile CRM package designed by Dexterity to communicate with engineers. New jobs are sent by email to the engineer's handheld computer, and the CRM software collects the information that used to be written on the FSR. This information can then be transmitted back to head office using Vodafone's high-speed GPRS mobile network.

Field technicians save an estimated 200 hours per day using the automated application. This has enabled the company to reduce headcount in the call centre, and redeploy some staff to more customer-facing roles.

your bank knows you've just moved house, that's CRM in action.

One of the areas where small and medium-sized enterprises (SMEs) can benefit most from CRM is in the field. Smaller businesses often rely heavily on personal customer service and support to differentiate themselves from bigger competitors, so improving the quality and responsiveness of sales and engineering staff can offer dramatic benefits.

Field service engineers and sales staff often use paper forms to record details of their work. In some businesses, staff might use laptops or handheld computers to record details into sales force automation software, which is essentially an electronic version of those paper forms.

Software providers are now combining customer relationship management with traditional sales force automation packages to offer on-the-road CRM. Adding wireless technology to the mix creates a powerful real-time customer service tool for smaller businesses.

what's on the market?

There is a range of products available to SMEs, costing from a few hundred pounds to many thousands. For example, the latest versions of Microsoft Office can cost as little as £150 and include basic customer contact management features. For a little more money you can get a separate customer management application. Larger companies, with 20 or more customer service staff, may want to consider a dedicated customer relationship management (CRM) package, which will link into finance, logistics and other business applications.

WEB-BASED CRM

Sansar Solutions, a UK-based electrical components retailer, sells its goods to customers all over the world. Many of its raw materials are sourced in the Far East, and staff regularly travel overseas to negotiate with potential suppliers. In a fiercely competitive industry, Sansar has to be faster and more responsive than the competition.

Details of new orders used to be recorded on paper forms and faxed to the head office. Now they are entered into a web-based CRM package provided by NetSuite. Sales staff connect to the application using wireless-enabled laptops and mobile phones, and enter details of orders the moment they are taken. Purchase orders and invoices are generated automatically, speeding up the sales cycle dramatically. Staff can also see at a glance what stock is available, and tell customers immediately how long an order will take to fulfil.

hosted packages

Until recently, this kind of technology wouldn't have been available to small companies such as Sansar Solutions. The cost of software licences, plus support, training and installation can easily reach six figures. However, most CRM vendors now offer to host software for smaller customers, providing them with access to the software over the Internet in return for a monthly subscription fee.

Hosted packages are ideal for SMEs that don't have the resources or the expertise to roll out software internally. And, they're generally 50 per cent cheaper than in-house software. Aspective, for example, offers a hosted Microsoft CRM application from £79 per user per month, plus Microsoft's licence fees.

When Crane Telecommunications, a Sussex-based distributor, rolled out a hosted CRM system from RightNow, cost was a key part of the decision. The

A MORE PROFESSIONAL SERVICE

Horwood Homewares supplies a wide range of household goods to some of the UK's best-loved home stores. The company employs 50 staff, including 10 mobile sales workers.

In 2003, Horwood wanted to provide mobile access to its CRM software to the sales team, and provided them with mobile data cards and company laptops. This allows the sales team to access information held in the company's IT systems.

Using the mobile CRM application means that staff don't need to call orders into the office to confirm product availability or to place orders on the system. Instead, they can access the latest order and stock information while still on site with customers.

Another benefit of the system is that staff can immediately generate an invoice with each sale, providing customers with faster service and quicker turnaround. This is done easily by using the laptop to connect to Windows 2000 Fax Wizard, which sends the order and invoice directly to the customer via fax.

The solution is a great success, says Justin Greenaway, IT systems manager at Horwood. "We've now got immediate access to crucial information and can provide a much better service to the customer," he says. "As a result, we look more professional and sales staff can be far more productive."

company, which has 150 employees, wanted to reduce operating costs following a global downturn in the telecoms sector. However, at the same time, it needed to improve its customer service. The hosted package was far cheaper than an internal system, and has the added advantage that the hosting company deals with issues such as security patches and software upgrades.

having a rationale

It's important to remember, though, that CRM software isn't a magic cure-all. Software might enable your business to automate all its customer processes, but you must consider whether that's actually a good idea. As a rule, you should carefully examine all your customer processes and make sure technology will improve both efficiency and effectiveness for customers. Also bear in mind that the software is only a tool.

A true CRM strategy should look at every point of interaction with the customer, and consider whether it can be improved. It could be that even the simplest of actions is required, such as getting sales staff to talk to secretaries on a first visit to collect information such as the office fax number, or when the firm's busy period is. Having that information upfront means you don't have to ask again, and that impresses the customer.

Despite what the salespeople might tell you, CRM software can only improve the efficiency of what you already do – it can't make your organisation more competitive or customer-friendly if the people and processes aren't in place to back it up. You'll need to invest in training to ensure that staff actually use the software for its intended purpose.

out in the field

Spotting those technologies that fit your business before competitors, while eschewing those that bring no real benefits, is the key trick when equipping field staff, says Philip Hunter, technology and business writer

Some workers are on the move so much that mobile communications are a must. If repair engineers and delivery drivers can contact base at any time, they can report instantly on their progress and request parts or follow-up, and take on new jobs as they come in. In public services, ambulance drivers and police officers without mobile communications would be unthinkable. For these people, the latest mobile solutions let them send the 'paperwork' directly without going back to base. For example, while on site, they can now fill in a form on their handheld device and get on with their next job. They can spend more time on the road, increase their productivity and improve their company's 'bottom line'.

EXECUTIVE SUMMARY

☐ key factors are the coverage required, the information needed and comparative costs

☐ profiling user requirements can control costs and boost staff productivity

☐ investment in technologies and software should be supported by the provision of technical training

varied requirements

Field sales and support cover many angles and bring diverse requirements for mobile communications, even within the orbit of a single SME. Field service staff may require BlackBerry™ type PDAs, while sales people might need full-blown laptop computers for presentations. Some tasks, such as meter reading, require dedicated devices to comply with security needs or reporting. The key factors for companies to consider are the coverage required, the information needed and the costs involved.

The choice of device type and network will vary according to user requirements. For North Wales Police Force, security is key. It uses handheld computers (PDAs) and mobile data tablets (MDTs) to access operational information 'in the field', allowing officers to spend more time on their primary policing duties. For organisations such as London's Natural History Museum, however, coverage is an important factor. The museum has a team of field archaeologists who collect information from all over world, which means that its networks need to have as wide a global coverage as possible – so it chose devices that were compatible with the services required.

Even when the geographical requirements are more modest, support for roaming will often be a major consideration, as networks vary both in their coverage and in the devices they support.

managing costs

Profiling mobile requirements can help identify recent or emerging technologies that could yield further cost savings or productivity gains. (This is covered more broadly in Chapter 5.) Location services is one such option, for they can pinpoint the whereabouts of field personnel instantly, making it easier to deploy them quickly and efficiently. There is even the potential for combining such location information with software that optimises the dispatch of engineers to jobs. Solutions to the famous 'travelling salesman problem', designed to find the shortest distance between a given set of destinations, could be combined with accurate locating of staff to cut wasted journey times.

Cost is clearly a major factor in the whole mobile equation, given that tariffs are higher than for fixed line communications, and that there is more potential for excessive use by employees in the field, both for business and personal purposes. It is, therefore, important to set guidelines for use of mobile devices, perhaps with limits over personal calls (see Chapter 8).

Such guidelines should be derived from a careful appraisal of every field employee's communication requirements. Mobile operators such as Vodafone can help with such user profiling, identifying the nature and level of communication requirement. This helps identify the device type for each user, and also provides aggregate information that can determine the network service package that

IMPROVED CONTROL OF COMPANY ASSETS

As a supplier of commercial refrigeration systems for the food industry including leading supermarkets, Space Cooling Systems relies heavily on its team of 160 field service engineers for on-site support and maintenance. Equipment failure must be dealt with promptly to minimise damage to perishable foods, and customers expect an engineer to arrive on site within four hours of an emergency call.

This means the company must organise the field service force so that there is always an engineer within range of every customer, while also ensuring that they are all kept busy. To achieve this the company has relied on mobile phones since its inception in 1988. But engineers are sometimes out of range of calls when on site, and have lacked the ability to report on their progress or provide the information needed to compile invoices for the work done. This delayed the payment of bills and meant engineers were not always routed quickly and efficiently to their next job, with a corresponding cost to the company.

Space Cooling Systems realised that mobile data communications would make it possible to provide real time interactivity between its head office, five area offices, and network of field engineers, through two-way 'always on' communications. The company installed Advatech SiCLOPS call-scheduling software connected via Vodafone GSM data services to Compaq iPaq PDAs carried by each engineer. Now engineers can pick up calls when they're ready and available for the next job, respond, and once the job is completed, send back details immediately. The central office has full information about each completed job available on screen and can generate invoices the same day.

Above all, the engineers are more visible to the central office rather than disappearing into black holes from which they may not emerge until a few hours later. According to Mark Aplin, Space Cooling Systems' Administration Manager for the SiCLOPS project, the Vodafone data network has provided a competitive edge in two ways. "Our customers are getting better levels of support, and it's definitely paying for itself through improved control of key company assets," he says. Furthermore bills are now going out on time.

minimises costs while providing the required level of functionality and coverage.

This is an important step given the large number of tariff options available, and requires information on the likely profile of usage. Field service engineers, for example, will often be communicating mostly with their own headquarters, in which case a package including an estimated number of internal calls or data sessions might be most effective.

Sales staff, on the other hand, may be communicating a lot with customers outside the organisation, so would most likely benefit from a package based on lower call charges.

TRACKING DOWN TAXIS

Zingo is a mobile phone taxi-hailing service that enables passengers to hail a nearby 'for hire' licensed London black cab by calling a national rate number from their mobile. Launched in April 2003, the service is already expanding and there are plans for more than 2,000 taxis to display the Zingo logo and telephone number.

The company teamed up with Vodafone to provide the service, which uses the operator's location-based services (LBS) data alongside the Global Positioning System (GPS) technology. The radio-pad in the taxi utilises Vodafone Paknet to send a continuous stream of GPS data. This locates the taxi while the customer call is being diverted to the cab driver, using Vodafone's Mobile Virtual Private Network service.

Driver and passenger are then connected so they can confirm the pick up point. Having arrived at the destination, the passenger can pay for the fare using a credit card, which is authorised by Vodafone's Paknet service. An automated terminal then prints a receipt.

This scenario illustrates how business users are increasingly relying on their mobile as an essential everyday device.

identifying training needs

Profiling also helps identify the training needs of mobile staff. This may include instruction on specific processes or IT applications, such as workflow to organise tasks effectively and fulfil reporting requirements (see Chapters 2 and 8). The example of Space Cooling Systems (see case study) highlights the fact that efficient deployment of field service engineers relies as much on timely use of the PDAs for reporting on location and work done, as it does on the data network. Training may also be needed to navigate through databases or support applications.

Security is another important aspect of training. Given the risk of theft or loss of portable devices it may be that staff should be instructed to download sensitive information to a central host in encrypted form and then delete it immediately from the mobile. Training may well also extend to mobile phone etiquette, which is covered more fully in chapter 8.

an office on the move

Employees out in the field can now have access to the same technologies and systems as their office-based colleagues, says Sandra Vogel, business and technology writer

For many companies a mobile office is a matter of necessity rather than choice, with the train, plane and taxi having to double as an office. For most of us that means carrying a laptop computer with all the usual software we'd expect to have when sitting in an office.

what is a mobile office?

The mobile professional office will vary from user to user, but there are some tools that almost every worker will require:

☐ standard word processing, spreadsheet, presentations and other software used within the office, along with all the documents relevant to current work

☐ an up-to-date diary and calendar

☐ email, with access to the inbox for viewing pre-existing emails, and the ability to send and receive new messages

☐ the web. This is vital for work-based research and is a valuable resource when liaising with clients

EXECUTIVE SUMMARY

☐ benefits of a mobile professional office include reduced paperwork, more efficient use of time and improved return on investment

☐ such an option also offers potential to improve the work-life balance

☐ teleworkers – although not strictly mobile workers – will make use of the same technology tools as their travelling counterparts

In addition to these essentials, there is likely to be a requirement for software and information that is specific to your role. Examples include secure mobile access to your Customer Relationship Management database, or to your company's intranet, with its important internal information.

benefits and productivity gains

Potential productivity and cost-efficiency benefits include:

- [ ] reduced paperwork, and reduced duplication of effort. A simple example is the completion of standard timesheets using a template document on a laptop. When data is shared with the office network, timesheet information is incorporated automatically into the central system. There is no paperwork, and no need for an administrator to key in the data

- [ ] greater time efficiency. For example, there are usually a number of 10 to 20 minute 'dead periods' in the day, such as time waiting for a train or for a meeting to begin. These can easily be used to deal with email, resulting in an hour or more of gained productivity each day

- [ ] an enhanced professional persona. Equipped with a laptop and access to your intranet you can show a potential client examples of work similar to what they require immediately, rather than offering to forward these examples at a later date

- [ ] improved return on investment. Purchasing a laptop for employees as their sole computer rather than both a desktop and a laptop has several advantages. These include lower hardware cost and more opportunity for 'hot desking' leading to reduced costs per employee and increased potential for an employee to work at more than one company office

A mobile office also offers potential health and welfare benefits. Rather than stretching working time into an evening to meet a deadline, employees can work while they're travelling between meetings. This way, the working day can be better contained, helping to maintain a reasonable work-life balance.

If you are a mobile professional office user with a duplicated system back at base, all the changes you make while on the move, such as generating emails or

RETRIEVING FILES AT A DISTANCE

Avivo is a marketing solutions agency that produces static and multimedia documents that can be large in size. Client liaison is crucial to the business, and account managers spend a lot of time at client premises demonstrating and working on projects.

Account managers use Vodafone's Mobile Connect 3G/GPRS data card with Apple Powerbook laptops to connect to office applications and retrieve files while at client's premises. "By using 3G, they can walk into a client's office, open their notebooks and download a 2-3Mb file in seconds," says Duncan Gardner, managing director.

The communications link is also used to access Avivo's intranet, which helps account managers establish the company to prospective new clients. And, it provides mobile access to standard office applications. "Last time I was stuck in traffic in a London taxi, I was able to do 50 minutes work on email using the Mobile Connect card," says Gardner.

producing documents, can be replicated on your main system. This can be achieved in a range of ways, either when you are in the office, or using various 'over the air' mobile communications. All you need is the appropriate software and communications technologies to allow this to happen.

Alternatively, access to some kinds of data, such as the corporate intranet, could be delivered by password-secured Virtual Private Networks. Such systems help maintain security, since no information is stored on the laptop itself.

Some mobile professionals simply require regular feeds of information. International law firm Ashurst, for example, uses BlackBerry™ devices to deliver email to 180 partners and other senior personnel who are on the move.

working from home

It's also possible to extend the mobile professional office concept to include working from home, or teleworking. Teleworking in itself is not, strictly speaking, a mobile professional office solution, in that teleworkers work from a fixed location which just happens to be their home rather than the office.

But teleworking does usually require provision of the standard work environment in a home situation, and teleworkers can divide their time in various ways – between home and a formal office and other locations. In such situations, fast

REMOTE ACCESS TO OFFICE NETWORKS

Hogg Robinson, international provider of corporate and employee services, uses different mobile office solutions depending on the needs of its staff.

Some staff use BlackBerry™ – a handheld mobile email device – while others use a data communications card with a laptop.

The data card and laptop combination provides users with access to their office networks from wherever they are. Users can connect to, and use, the company's intranet, email and standard office applications such as Microsoft PowerPoint and Excel. Users can also use the Web.

The BlackBerry™ device is more suited to those for whom email is the key mobile office application. These devices can collect email automatically both in the UK and abroad, while its small keyboard can be used to compose replies.

In both cases always-on GPRS connections are used, so that access to the required services is constantly available.

Internet connections such as broadband can be used along with special software to ensure data on the home computer mirrors that in the office.

Just like other forms of mobile professional office work, teleworking can be cost effective. Take East Midlands Electricity, which has around 150 of the 400 employees who telework anywhere between one day a week to a full week. Staff have laptops as their main computers. It has been estimated that over three years each teleworker could save the company around £3,500.

simple solutions

The key drivers behind making any office mobile, whatever its complexity, are the corresponding aims of improving productivity and maximising cost-efficiency. For some companies this will mean investing in more advanced technology such as laptops, data cards or mobile epos systems. Mobile offices can utilise these and many other sophisticated mobile 'tools'.

But for many small to medium sized businesses, simply making better use of familiar existing functions such as text messaging and voicemail – without any additional capital expenditure – can bring worthwhile benefits.

mobile commerce

M-commerce offers businesses an abundance of opportunities, says Marc Ambasna-Jones, business and technology writer

To date, many businesses have been put off mobile commerce because of a combination of misinformation and poor perception.

This means that, so far, the technology has found a home primarily in the consumer space, enabling the mobile hungry youth market to download the latest ringtones and games. But, there is a place here for businesses too, whether buying or selling.

Currently, business-related services for mobile phone users are limited. Until now, the main business applications for the mobile

EXECUTIVE SUMMARY

☐ mobile commerce (m-commerce) is the term used to describe buying or selling goods and services via mobile devices and networks

☐ businesses can tap into existing services and look forward to new applications such ticketing and location-based services

☐ wireless technologies have a future in helping businesses utilise the potential of m-commerce in retail environments

that demand some form of payment are news and information services such as AA Roadwatch and location-based services such as mobile and asset tracking. Using such services, businesses can improve journey planning – saving time and money – and access instant information on the location of staff, vehicles or goods, which can improve customer service. These services can be purchased through operator-specific mobile payment systems, such as Vodafone's m-pay service, which allows users to pay for goods and services directly from their handset – the amount can be debited from their credit card or added to their mobile bill.

Businesses should also think of m-commerce as an opportunity if they are suppliers of goods and services. It could offer them another means of transacting sales and getting their marketing message to potential cutomers.

changing attitudes

Most operators have some form of multimedia portal from which their customers can buy a range of products and services. These are usually provided by both the operator and third-party merchants and will enhance the handset and general mobile communications experience. This development, together with the proliferation of powerful multimedia handsets, is making users change the way they think about the mobile.

In understanding the role that m-commerce can play it's important to ignore all the old hype and think of it as an enabling technology. It's not an application but a mechanism that enables mobile phone users to pay for a range of services.

Changing attitudes to the mobile is critical to the whole process as businesses need to see beyond the hype and current limitations. It's important to consider the opportunities that will come about in the next few years, which could provide businesses with potential differentiators and sales opportunities. Take mobile ticketing, the purchase and redemption of tickets using the mobile phone, which is one growth area. Imagine a system where employee expense accounts are automatically debited via mobile purchases of train tickets. This is already happening in Japan through NTT DoCoMo.

There are also car parking trials underway around the country where users can pay for tickets via SMS. One such trial is car park operator Park Mobile in London. Another is mPark in Edinburgh. For the moment, the pricing models do not make them competitive with the traditional cash-based system.

cross industry co-operation

Using the mobile to buy physical goods and services from retail stores using mobile payment is still in early development, as it demands a tremendous amount of cross industry co-operation to forge standards (see box opposite).

Simpay, is one example of a joint venture involving Orange, Telefonica Moviles, T-Mobile and Vodafone, but this is not a standard as such. Rather, it is a drive to create an interoperable mobile payment mechanism for operators.

RFID OFFERS PAYMENT UTILISATION POTENTIAL

Radio Frequency Identification (RFID) has become a major buzz term in the IT and telecoms industries. Its role as a tracking technology within retail supply chains is well-documented but it also has potential as an m-commerce enabling technology for retail.

While this may seem 'pie in the sky', many businesses are taking it very seriously. MasterCard with its PayPass (www.paypass.com) trial is adding to the general interest and application of RFID in mobile payments. Contactless credit cards are an attractive proposition for credit card companies as they are more secure than the magnetic swipe type and RFID is one of the technologies that can enable the contactless capability.

In May 2003, Nokia joined up with MasterCard to integrate its PayPass technology into its phones. Nokia has been trialling the technology with a group of retailers in Irving, Texas. Consumers tap or wave their Nokia mobile phone over a special RFID reader at the point of sale to make a payment. The reader then identifies, authorises and deducts payments from the credit card number provided.

Nokia is no stranger to linking RFID m-commerce. It has already trialled RFID-enabled phones using an RFID chip embedded into a SmartCover for its 5100 Series. The trial was conducted in 2001 with 2Scoot and enabled customers at restaurants to have their phones scanned by RFID and their payments authorised immediately via 2Scoot's network.

The Mobey Forum has also been working on the implementation of RFID. As part of its Preferred Payment Architecture for local payments specification, the standards body demonstrated an RFID-enabled POS in Q3 2002, using the mobile phone as the payment device.

Since these early trials, a number of Mobey Forum members, including Nordea Bank, Nokia and Visa, have been participating in an RFID pilot trial in Finland. The pilot will study the consumers' and merchants' experiences in the RFID payment environment. The results are currently under evaluation and expected to be published in 2005.

For traditional retailing it's more complicated, as retail organisations, the banking and credit communities, the mobile operators, handset vendors and retail POS technology developers, all have to agree on the best way forward.

It is a lengthy process of trials and discussion, but it will happen in some form. The premise is a simple one: individuals are increasingly likely to carry a mobile, so why not use it as a wallet or payment device too? According to Juniper Research, the global market for m-commerce transactions is expected to reach $87bn by 2009, so there has to be mileage in mobile commerce for businesses. It is just a case of picking the right moment and application, and that applies to whether you are a user, developer or potential retail trader.

Connect to a hotspot and download attachments before your coffee gets cold.

The Vodafone 3G data card's software now recognises WiFi connectivity, making it even simpler to connect to a hotspot. And with easy billing, you can quickly download email attachments, browse the internet and get company files at near-office speeds. Just don't spill your coffee. To find out how we make mobile working work with WiFi, call 0800 587 8057 or visit your local Vodafone Store.

Our fast 3G data card now works with WiFi.

technology
explained

How do you work your way through the vast array of mobile technology choices? Steve Gold, business and technology writer, sets out the options

Mobile technologies have advanced rapidly since people first started using mobile phones 20 years ago.

EXECUTIVE SUMMARY

☐ there are two types of GSM mobile data services – GPRS and HSCSD

☐ 3G cellular services are based on a cluster of standards, and operate at higher frequencies than GSM

☐ company use of Wi-Fi technology is increasing in the UK

☐ Bluetooth has been called the poor relation of Wi-Fi, but it also supports voice, as well as data, and is less expensive

☐ integration of different types of mobile communication will lead to a new generation of devices

GSM – global system for mobile communications

First seen in the early nineties, GSM is one of the world's great technology success stories, mainly thanks to the pressing need amongst businesses and consumers for a mobile phone system that works reliably when within coverage. GSM is a digital mobile telephone system that is widely used in Europe and other parts of the world.

GSM's piece de resistance is the fact that it allows users to roam between countries, with users receiving the bill (or paying as they go) in their home country. This makes the system very useful for travellers.

The cellular technology now has a billion-plus users around the world in more than 200 countries, having grown from a million users across Europe in 1993.

GSM is both ubiquitous and low-cost and it remains a perfect business aid for use when travelling for voice calls and text messaging.

Most of the world uses GSM networks that operate at 900 and 1800 megahertz, but North America uses GSM operating at 1900 megahertz. This means that GSM roamers wanting to use US or Canadian GSM networks must use a tri-band (ie. GSM 900/1800/1900) mobile phone.

Although most mobile phones these days are tri-band, some are not, so users need to check their mobile supports GSM 1900 before they travel to North America. If their mobile does not support GSM 1900, then an upgrade or phone rental through their operator can be easily arranged. Today's GSM mobiles are multi-functional, supporting voice, text messaging, mobile Internet and email facilities on handsets that sell for the same cost as a night in a business motel.

One feature the industry is developing is the use of GSM (and 3G) mobiles on aircraft, using very lower power transmitters. As well as supporting voice calls on aircraft, the technology will also allow limited mobile data facilities, such as access to text messaging and email services.

mobile data – GPRS

GPRS and HSCSD (High Speed Circuit Switched Data) are two types of mobile GSM data transmission, the former being suitable for mobile Internet and email services, the latter more suited for dialling-up 'virtual private network' applications, such as secure access to a company network.

GPRS (General Packet Radio Service) is a way of sending and receiving information via a mobile phone or data card. Using GPRS is like having a permanent Internet connection rather than needing to 'dial up' every time. Because GPRS works in a different way to standard GSM services, it is also charged in a different way. Users can take as long as they want to write emails or browse information. They are only charged for the amount of information the device sends or receives, which means that reading and thinking time are free of charge.

3G (third generation) mobile services

First generation (1G) was analogue, second generation (2G) is digital, with some people referring to GPRS as an interim 2.5G state. Third generation (3G) cellular services use slightly higher frequencies than GSM, allowing base stations to be sited closer together. This, in turn, allows network operators to make better usage of the available frequency resources and offer much faster mobile data speeds, so supporting video calling, watching films and playing video games.

3G devices will send and receive data over 40 times faster than second generation networks. These speeds are expected to increase still further later in the decade, but for the moment, 3G is getting close to offering a wireless broadband service to many areas.

The UK's first 3G operator, Hutchison, or 3, launched its service in the spring of 2003, but only offers a controlled range of mobile Internet services, known in the industry as a 'walled garden'. Mobile data services on 3 are not expected until later in 2005. All four of the UK GSM operators, in contrast, already offer 3G data services, with Vodafone having launched its 3G consumer voice service in November 2004, with no fewer than 10 3G handsets. You can expect prices to fall as the technology is more widely adopted.

Wi-Fi (wireless fidelity, or wireless local networking)

Wi-Fi technology uses various wireless standards to support short-range (up to 100 metres in the open) mobile broadband speeds. Faster than 3G, Wi-Fi is a non-cellular system, meaning you have to be stationary in relation to the transmitter to use it. It is available in two types – private (office and home) and public (out and about) – and is a low-cost delivery mechanism for mobile broadband in and outside buildings.

Wi-Fi cards for notebook computers and PDAs (personal digital assistants) now cost around £50. Wi-Fi is available in multiple 'flavours', with most public Wi-Fi networks using 802.11b technology. The dominant public Wi-Fi operator in the UK is BT Openzone (www.btopenzone.com), which has expanded by securing roaming agreements with other operators. Usage costs approximately £25 a month ongoing, or £40 for a one-off month, for a maximum of 4,000 minutes. Pay-as-you-go at 20 pence per minute is also available.

Wi-Fi is increasingly being seen on long-distance trains in the UK, allowing train operators to support near-broadband mobile data services as an additional benefit for their customers. Economies of scale mean that it usually cheaper for rail travellers to use a train-based Wi-Fi service than use a standard GPRS connection, especially since the railways usually offer Wi-Fi service free to their first class customers, both on the train and at stations. Behind the scenes, the train operators use a combination of multiple GPRS and satellite channels to ensure customers' mobile data connections remain unbroken.

bluetooth

Bluetooth is a short-range personal area network technology, and was originally designed for voice communications over 10 to 100 feet, rather than mobile data (which Wi-Fi was developed for). However, it has now become a useful means of wirelessly connecting two voice devices, eg. a mobile phone and headset or mobile phone and notebook.

Some sources suggest that Wi-Fi is a competitor to Bluetooth. In fact, the two technologies are complementary, not just between themselves, but to other 'wireless' services such as GPRS and 3G.

Bluetooth operates in the same waveband as 802.11b Wi-Fi. It is slower (721 kilobits per second) but uses less power and its electronics are currently much smaller. Because of this advantage, Bluetooth 'chipsets' are routinely included in mobile phones. There is also an Enhanced Data Rate version of Bluetooth on the drawing board that will triple the data speeds, yet reduce the power required still further.

Internet telephony

It is possible to conduct voice conversations over the Internet, and this includes mobile Internet solutions. There are two options to consider: voice over GPRS and voice over Wi-Fi. The network operators market voice over GPRS as 'push-to-talk'. Calls made using this technology are relatively cheap, especially when roaming. It will shortly be possible to use push-to-talk technology to place a call back to your office colleagues, bypassing the regular phone network altogether. The potential cost savings, particularly when roaming, are significant.

Mobile Internet telephony services are expected to take off during 2005 with various operators promoting their voice over Wi-Fi services using Wi-Fi-based cordless phones and Internet telephony-enabled notebooks/PDAs as an alternative to making phone calls when out and about. Although not as mobile as GSM cellular, voice over Wi-Fi services are likely to become popular, both when out and about, as well as in office environments.

One of the most interesting applications of voice over Wi-Fi is the home office with broadband, as it effectively gives users a second phone line without the expense of installing and paying rental on the second line. This 'second line' can be dedicated for use as a business line, allowing home office workers to clearly separate their work and leisure calls.

convergent communications

Close levels of integration between the different forms of mobile communications is likely to drive a new generation of mobile devices, which will offer users a choice of communications pathways for any given task, be it making calls, checking email, etc.

Vodafone already supports this trend with its notebook PC software for its 3G/2.5G data card. The Vodafone Mobile Connect card is currently available in a format suitable for both PC and Mac notebook computers.

Vodafone has extended the Dashboard/Communicator software facilities as more network topologies (eg. Wi-Fi) are integrated into a mobile device card. The software now gives users a choice of speed against costs, as different users have different needs when it comes to mobile communications, as well as a single bill for each accounting period.

messaging services

Alongside GSM, 3G, Wi-Fi and the myriad other mobile voice and data technologies, a range of text and data services for mobile networks has been developed. The most fundamental of these is the Short Message Service (SMS) which enables users to send or receive short text-only messages of up to 160 characters to or from a mobile phone. SMSs can now also be sent between fixed and mobile phones, and to and from PCs. The Multimedia Messaging Service (MMS) is a modification of SMS technology, and allows attachments to be routed to and from mobiles. This service allows for non real-time transmission of various services, such as video and audio clips.

location services

Many networks, both 2G (GSM) and 3G, are offering location-based services to their customers. These services use the low-tech method of pin-pointing which cellular base station the user is currently accessing to give an indication of where they are.

Because all mobiles have the ability to monitor several cellular base stations in their vicinity – to allow a call to be 'handed off' between base stations in a controlled manner – it is now possible to 'triangulate' a user to a few tens of metres in a city area. Several firms are therefore offering mobile location services to companies as a low-cost alternative to GPS satellite location.

As 3G services take off, location-based services will start to look very attractive, allowing a company, for example, to automatically start pushing an employee's email to their mobile when they move beyond the confines of the office. Business travellers can already use location-based services to quickly find facilities, such as bank ATMs, hotels and restaurants, in their vicinity. Although still in their infancy, such services are developing rapidly and can make life a great easier for travellers of all types.

mobile devices

The distinction between mobile phones, smartphones and PDAs has blurred considerably since the first GSM handsets and Windows-driven (and Palm) PDAs started shipping in the early nineties. The reasons for this are the advanced software seen on smartphones and the communications technology that has been added to PDAs.

While PDAs have steadily increased in their communications abilities, battery power has, until recently, held back the development of smartphones. Now the latest generation of smartphones have all but licked the battery power issue, and most units have standby times measured in several days, approaching that of a standard GSM mobile.

The mainstream mobile phone vendors are also releasing models with PDA functionality, such as SonyEricsson's popular P800, 900 and 910 series. The P910 even has a miniature QWERTY-style keyboard under its flap, as well as Bluetooth facilities and over-the-air synchronisation facilities with a host PC.

Just to make life interesting, a third category of mobile device, the email handset, has arrived from Research in Motion (RIM), known as the BlackBerry™.

Optimised for mobile email, the BlackBerry™ series uses data compression technology to minimise users' GPRS bills. The latest BlackBerry,™ the 7100v from Vodafone, has moved away from the mini-QWERTY keyboards on earlier models, and replaced it with a proprietary keyboard. Using this approach has allowed RIM to shrink the handset to a pocketable 120 grams.

The BlackBerry™ has enjoyed some success in the business arena, as the email handsets are optimised for email first, and other facilities second.

Most BlackBerry™ devices can interwork with various email systems from Internet service providers (ISPs), as well as company servers (Exchange and Notes), which makes them suitable for almost any business size. All the units also allow mobile Internet surfing, as well as voice calls, but these are additional functions to the main email facility.

On the PDA front, the market is split into PocketPC (the latest version of Windows CE) and Palm camps. The former operating system has the advantage of being developed by Microsoft and is desktop Windows-friendly. Palm, on the other hand, pioneered the low-cost PDA industry and all of its models, including the feature-laden units, remain excellent value for money, especially the Tungsten series, several of which include Wi-Fi (802.11b) support as standard.

Now the big question is: which device is best? The answer lies in what facilities you want while on the road. If your needs are mainly for voice communications, with email a close second, then a smartphone such as the BlackBerry™ 7100v from Vodafone would appear the best option.

If your needs are for mobile email and PDA functions on the move, with voice a close second, then a PocketPC or Palm-driven PDA may be more appropriate.

With all the UK's operators now also offering 3G mobile data, a 3G voice mobile may be appropriate, linking to a PDA using Bluetooth, acting as a mobile modem for the PDA (or notebook PC) in question. The advantage of this Bluetooth connectivity strategy is that the 3G mobile can remain in your pocket or briefcase, yet still act as a wireless modem when needed.

Using Bluetooth's personal area network technology also means your mobile office kit can be modular, with parts of it upgradeable as and when is necessary. You can also use the Bluetooth connectivity on your mobile phone to interface wirelessly with a Bluetooth car kit.

Notebook PC users can also use a 3G data card that fits into the PCMCIA slot on their machine. These cards have the slight advantage that they are under the direct control of the notebook PC, rather than relying on a Bluetooth or similar connection, and will support 3G, GPRS and, in some cases, Wi-Fi.

company voice/data integration

As companies replace their Private Branch Exchange (PBX) systems, they are choosing increasingly to integrate the PBX function with their network/intranet facilities. This also tends to coincide with a full or partial migration of internal voice communications to an alternative infrastructure.

From a user's perspective, this means that the desktop phone interfaces with the desktop PC, usually going through the same cabling point in the wall. From a company perspective, there are also significant opportunities for cost savings, particular if in-country and international branch voice communications traffic is involved.

One feature that many company communications managers overlook is the high level of integration that is possible between mobile and PBX users. This integration – known as 'Office' facilities – allows desktop PBX features, such as call-back-when-free and multi-extension ringing, to be extended to include mobile users. The operators are able to offer these services, thanks to high-level switching between the cellular network and the customer's office PBX system.

Businesses can also cut the cost of their PBX-to-mobile calls using leased circuits from their offices to the nearest access point on a mobile operator's network (usually a base station). In addition, some companies are moving over to Internet Protocol (IP) –based PBXs, which have the ability to route all calls, both voice and data, across a single line to a single desktop device, typically an office PC with an integral advanced software-driven phone fitted as standard.

the future beckons

Just as GSM revolutionised the cellular industry in the early 1990s, 3G is starting to change the way users view their mobile phone. Like GSM, however, it is down to the networks how they market their 3G services to the public, meaning it could be several years before we see the 'killer applications' on 3G that caused GSM to take off in the mid-1990s.

Looking back, GSM usage took off largely thanks to the introduction of innovative tariffs, text messaging and pay-as-you-go accounts. Coupled within access to mobile data and international roaming, GSM has become ubiquitous.

Today, we have multiple wireless technology standards – 3G, Bluetooth, Wi-Fi etc – jostling for users' attention and budgets. It looks certain that, no matter how 3G is offered to the public, it will become one wireless network system among several. Tomorrow's mobile phones and devices will use multiple networks, including 3G, to satisfy their users' voice and mobile data needs.

The operators are investing heavily in their various networks and are racing to make 3G as ubiquitous in coverage terms as GSM. Users are also expecting good public access Wi-Fi coverage, as well as mobile devices that support mobile Internet/email access, for around the same monthly budget they paid out for GSM in the late 1990s.

It will come down to the marketing, rather than the technical, prowess of the networks to achieve this objective. The good news for users is that high levels of competition will help to keep upfront, as well as ongoing, costs in check. And that is no bad thing.

setting company policies

It is essential that employers state in writing what employees can and can't do with business-owned mobile tools, says Marc Ambasna-Jones, business and technology writer

Understanding and controlling mobile communications usage within an organisation is essential. If there are no company policies in place, costs can rise and obstruct the real benefits of implementing mobile voice and data solutions.

EXECUTIVE SUMMARY

☐ businesses need to implement mobile phone policies to ensure a fair and cost-effective system for both the company and its employees

☐ as well as covering personal use, policies should look at roaming, health and safety, security/confidentiality, upgrade cycles and even phone etiquette

☐ price plans are becoming more business-focused, making mobile use more attractive to businesses

☐ policies should be updated in line with increased mobile usage

people, policy, procedure

Every business has its own working practices, requirements and tolerances, so a 'one-size-fits-all' approach is not appropriate. All businesses, however, would be wise to consider the following three key questions:

☐ **people**
Who will be provided with a device, and what training with they receive?

☐ **policy**
How prescriptive do you need to be?

☐ **procedures**
How will you implement or enforce your policy equally among staff?

Core issues for most small and medium sized businesses include:

☐ **who?**

The first and most obvious consideration is to identify the essential users within the business? You need to make sure you're not paying for devices and calls unnecessarily. On the other hand, members of staff who need a device also need to know how to apply for one.

☐ **what?**

What does each user need to help get the job done? Field support, for example, may require BlackBerry™ email devices. Logistics may need to carry a standard GSM mobile for asset tracking purposes, while management may need notebooks with 3G cards (see chapter 2). Who has access to email, or needs access? Who has access to enterprise applications such as sales order processing? Can users make personal calls? (For example, some companies restrict personal calls to emergencies only, others state 'fair usage'.) How can personal and business calls be separated (particularly in terms of the VAT requirement)? What is reasonable use? What material may staff access – and does this link into any email/Internet policy? What disciplinary action will be taken for excessive or inappropriate use?

☐ **how?**

Decide how the device will be purchased and distributed. Will you allow people to expense back their work related calls or will you provide them with a work phone? By buying devices in bulk you could obtain better pricing and control the upgrade cycle, but some companies prefer to give their employees a budget and leave them to it. Stating who is responsible for purchasing avoids unnecessary confusion. Where devices – and security passwords – remain company property, staff will have a duty to protect confidential information. (See chapter 9)

☐ **when?**

How often is the usage reviewed? How often should someone receive an upgrade? What happens on leaving the company? Who has ownership of the phone and will an employee be allowed to keep it when they leave?

having a policy handbook

These questions may seem basic, but it's so often the simple things, the critical non-essentials, that can collectively have a massive impact on a business. It's important that every individual within the organisation is made aware of what the parameters are for mobile usage – and therefore every company should explain them clearly in a policy handbook. Thereafter, employees should be sent regular reminders of the importance of complying with the policies, perhaps alongside updates on their usage.

health and safety

Health and safety should be at the forefront of any company's policy. Are employees aware of health and safety issues and legal requirements? Stating in writing that you expect your employees to abide by the law is essential. Forcing employees to make or receive calls while driving, for example, is against the law. If you don't cover this rather crucial health and safety aspect in a policy, and your employee is involved in an accident as a result of using a mobile phone, then the business could be liable too.

It is worth pointing out that holding a device while driving is illegal, as it can cause the driver to be distracted. An alternative is to use a hands-free kit that attaches the device to the dashboard, where voice recognition can be used. This is less likely to distract a driver than the use of a portable hands-free kit. (See chapter 9).

mixing business with pleasure

It is key to have a policy on personal calls. Obviously, the motivation behind the deployment of mobile devices should determine the policy. So if the motivation is for individuals to keep in contact with the office and other members of the business while on the road, then that should be in the policy.

Having a set monthly mobile telephony fee and ensuring the business works within the stated parameters can help in monthly budgeting and expenditure forecasting. Many operators can also help in breaking down personal calls and providing a system by which they can be identified and calculated

BUILDING A COMPANY POLICY

Every business will be different but here are some must-have points for the policies:

- [ ] identification: who in the business needs mobile voice and data? What devices/services do they need to help them be more productive? How will products and services be purchased and distributed?

- [ ] ownership: it's easy for users to forget who owns the device and rules on mobile maintenance could ensure that you get the most out of your investment before it needs upgrading. For example, have some rules on looking after devices, keeping them safe and clean

- [ ] health and safety: demand that employees abide by the law and don't drive while using a hand-held mobile

- [ ] personal calls: define what the business will tolerate. No-one wants to rule employees with an iron rod so there must be some fair way of establishing reasonable use for personal calls

- [ ] roaming: international roaming can lead to expensive calls, so outline who needs it and what the rules are

automatically. This is now a requirement for VAT audits as the VAT office and VAT legislation provides for assessment.

Businesses cannot recover VAT on any purchases or expenses that are solely used for non-business purposes. When there is private and business use, then a 'fair and reasonable' apportionment should be made. These rules apply to items such as laptops and PDAs as well as mobile phones.

training and support

Given the increasing complexity of mobile voice and data devices and applications, offering employees training should also be a policy item. This will show commitment from the company in helping staff operate their 'tools' to their full potential, as well as minimising costly, time-wasting errors. Knowing how to send and receive email on a smartphone, send text messages, access and input items onto a calendar or even access office-based applications such as databases all need to be taught. Levels of training will vary, as will methods and trainers, but it is important that the policy commits the company to a frequency and type of training that will support staff in fulfilling their role.

roaming

Employees may need to travel and require international roaming on their mobile phones. The policy should include a section on roaming, how to lift barring, and expected use of the mobile while overseas. Will you offer voice-only roaming or will you allow data too, such as accessing email and mobile Internet sites?

mobile phone etiquette

The policy should require considerate use of a mobile or mobile device, covering such issues as the use of loud ringtones in the office and appropriate styles of greeting and messaging – including both text and voicemail.

It is vital that where staff liaise with customers they do so politely and efficiently, without leaving messages that cause annoyance. Equally, staff may be advised to use their handsets considerately in public places. It is well known how some companies' reputations have been dented by inconsiderate driving by field service or delivery staff, and boorish mobile phone use could have an equally damaging effect.

good practice

The bottom line is that written company policies provide a guide for new and existing employees of expected behaviour and use of company assets. A written policy can be easily referred to and, in some cases, act as an insurance policy for businesses against individual malpractice. It is important to keep revisiting policies too, as technology and the demands on devices and services from the business change. Providing a living 'rule' book for every aspect of the business is basically good company practice. Mobile technologies are now an integral part of working life and have to be included.

knowing the law

What legal issues are raised by mobile working, and how should these be addressed? Malcolm Wheatley, business and technology writer, outlines the key areas

Mobile working imposes legal and compliance requirements upon both employers and their employees. The main considerations to bear in mind fall under the following headings:

- ☐ health and safety and the mobile workplace

- ☐ mobile workers and driving

- ☐ data protection requirements

- ☐ Working Time Directive compliance

- ☐ tax implications

health and safety

EXECUTIVE SUMMARY

- ☐ employers should have a precise definition of what a mobile workplace is in order to fulfil their health and safety obligations properly

- ☐ there are two provisions within the Data Protection Act that apply to mobile working

- ☐ employers and employees need to be clear about where the normal place of employment is, as this has implications for travel expenses

Under the UK's health and safety legislation, the employer has an obligation to carry out a risk assessment of all health and safety issues that affect the workplace. The risk assessment must, therefore, include employees on the move.

"For example, where an employer requires his staff to drive as part of their job, the car becomes part of the workplace, and so is covered by the legislation," says Belinda Lester, a solicitor in the employment law group at law firm Sprecher Grier Halberstam LLP. The assessment, she explains, should cover the type of vehicle used, the type of driving that is required, and the provision made for mobile communications – such as hands-free car kits – while driving or in the vehicle.

Of equal importance is to have defined what the mobile workplace is exactly, says Rustom Tata, a partner and head of employment law at law firm DMH. Invariably, he says, mobile working and home working overlap, so the risk assessment should also cover the mobile employee's home, if he or she works there regularly.

Many middle-ranking and senior employees stay in touch from home, using a desk, computer and mobile phone to check messages, download email and carry out administrative chores, such as filing expense claims.

It is the employer's responsibility, says Tata, to make sure that the risks associated with this have been assessed. "You can't just get the employee to certify that their home is safe: it's the employer's responsibility to make sure that a risk assessment has been undertaken," he says. "You can send the IT department to carry it out, or outsource it, but you can't just walk away from it."

mobile workers and driving

Employers need to be particularly careful when considering the use of mobile devices by employees in company vehicles or while on company business. Driving while using a handheld phone is of course illegal. Drivers can also be prosecuted for not having safe control of the vehicle – so even if they are using a hands-free device, if its use is considered to have contributed to an accident, they could still be prosecuted under existing legislation.

All new employment contracts drawn up on behalf of clients by Ashfords, a firm of solicitors, now include a clause relating to mobile telephony, says assistant solicitor Chloë Minchington. "Essentially, it says that employees are prohibited from making calls while driving unless the vehicle is equipped with a hands-free kit, and that doing so will constitute gross misconduct and may result in instant dismissal," she says.

Some employers go further and make it clear in their policies that mobile telephones should not be used at all while driving, aware of the risk that the employer as well as the employee can be prosecuted in the event of an accident. "It might be surprising for employers to realise that prosecution by the Health & Safety Executive in relation to the lack of a risk assessment, or the failure to have appropriate policies in place is far more serious than the risk of a fine for the employee actually falling foul of the regulations," says Belinda Lester.

data protection requirements

There are two provisions within the Data Protection Act that apply to mobile working. The most significant one is the so-called 7th Principle of Data Protection, says Dino Wilkinson, a solicitor with law firm Kimbells LLP. Essentially, he says, it requires employers to take appropriate organisational and technical measures to protect personal data from unlawful processing, accidental loss, destruction or damage.

However, he stresses, the Act only covers personal data, as distinct from corporate data. So, for example, spreadsheets, inventory records and the like are not covered by the Act, but fellow employees' names, addresses and other details are, as is information on suppliers, customers, and any other named individual.

How is an organisation to protect itself? Password protection is better than nothing, says Wilkinson, but encryption is preferable. Better still is to have policies in place governing the information that may be stored on mobile devices away from the secure IT environment of the formal workplace.

The 8th Principle of Data Protection, which covers the transfer of personal information to countries with inadequate data protection laws, applies only to employees whose business travel takes them outside the European Union, according to Michael Stinson, a principal consultant with IT security consultancy Diagonal Security. If employees work overseas alongside foreign nationals for long periods, he advises, beware of them slipping into informally sharing data on individuals as this would constitute a technical breach.

What's more, advises Lester, an organisation that is worried about this possibility can consider covering the issue in its data protection policy, and obtain an 'opt-in' approval relating to the transferring of data to other jurisdictions. In such an instance, the duty of protection would still apply, but at least permission to take the data overseas would have been obtained.

Working Time Directive compliance

Employers of mobile workers also need to consider their obligations under the Working Time Directive, which places a limit of 48-hours per week (averaged over 17 weeks), on the length of an employee's working week – even if they are based out of the office. "The onus is on the employee to keep a record of the hours that they work," advises Jon Keeble, employment law partner at Ricksons law firm.

In practice, he adds, employers' interest in their mobile employees' working hours should extend beyond mere compliance. Consistently working long hours has proven health and safety ramifications, and employers need to be cognisant of this. "There's a danger of people working too hard, with employees overworking to compensate for not being as visible as non-mobile workers," he says.

tax implications

While most employers and employees are aware of the tax legislation surrounding the use of employer-provided cars and employer-provided mobile phones, there are other issues that need to be considered, says Brian Lovie, director of remuneration and benefits at PKF, a firm of accountants and business advisers.

It's important, he says, that both the employer and employee makes clear where the normal place of employment is. If an employee can opt to work from home, then this will be insufficient grounds to persuade the Inland Revenue that an employee is 'mobile from home'. In such circumstances, then, the starting point for the calculation of travel expenses – to visit a client or customer, for example – would be the employer's normal place of work, even if this involved the employee incurring travel costs that could not be recovered.

"If you can get the Inland Revenue to accept that an employee is home-based, then every journey is chargeable. But to do this, you need to ensure that the employment contract states that the employee is home-based."

To conclude, it is important to stress that both employers' and employees' circumstances differ widely – and professional advice should be sought before acting on any of the legal or taxation issues raised in this chapter.

what will the future look like?

> Where does mobile go from here? What new products and technologies are on their way? Peter Judge, business and technology writer, offers an insight

During the next five years, our working lives will change fast. As with previous changes, this one will be driven by – and impact on – our whole lifestyle. But unlike previous changes, this time round it will be fuelled by technologies that are coming out of the private world and into the corporate world.

the consumer will be driving change

"Consumer technology is driving changes in ways it never has before," says John Mahoney, chief of research and IT management for the Gartner Group in Europe. Business people are increasingly being introduced to new technologies by mobile phone companies and gadget makers, he says.

EXECUTIVE SUMMARY

- [ ] consumer technology is driving the change that will be seen in the business world
- [ ] mobile workers will be able to access numerous applications, but it will be simpler for them than at present
- [ ] staff productivity will increase as their mobile tools will make their working lives more efficient – and more enjoyable

The future will see the big ideas being more likely to come from senior colleagues, rather than from the IT managers and 'techies' who tended to be at the forefront of innovation in the past.

technology that extends the 'self'

Consumers are beginning to see technology as an extension of themselves.

- ☐ They carry their phone everywhere, and forget the wired phone they have at home.
- ☐ They use text messages to keep in touch.
- ☐ They use instant messenger to let people know when they are available.
- ☐ They share images and thoughts in public diaries and weblogs.

For the last few years, business people have begun to bring that kind of thinking to work, using Palms and BlackBerry™ organisers. Now, those kind of devices are permeating everyday life, and the way of using them will sweep through business.

This has some big consequences. Unlike previous technology revolutions, it may be technology-based, but it won't be technology-oriented. "As a user, I don't give a damn what technology is behind it," says analyst Clive Longbottom of QuoCirca. "It's incumbent on the vendor to get everything sorted out."

In five years, you won't worry what protocol your business communication is using, any more than a consumer thinks about how their text message gets from person 'a' to person 'b'.

This means that you can treat the big debates in the technology field as background noise. Ignore the details and look at the overall direction.

what network? who cares?

Take the somewhat convoluted example of communications networks. There are many technologies, and more coming along (like Wi-Fi, WiMax and 3G). It may sound like the future is complicated.

In fact, it is the present that is complicated. The future will be less so.

"Look at what you are carrying now," says Longbottom. "You probably have a laptop, a phone and a PDA. The phone and the laptop may have 3G, the laptop and the PDA will have Wi-Fi, and all three may have Bluetooth."

"Believe it or not, you are probably carrying around seven or eight radios," he says. "You only need one. In future, your devices won't have a hard radio," says Longbottom. "They will have a soft radio that can handle all the different ways to connect."

The next big thing won't get rid of what is there already. It will aggregate and blend it, and merge it all into one service. That radio will spot the communications available, and load up the software to use it – without bothering you.

In five years' time, the device you carry in your pocket or briefcase will just get the best data connection it can at any given moment, and use it to support whatever job you are doing at that time.

If you are on a phone call, and walk into the office, the call will transfer automatically off the cell network and onto your office LAN. And you will not know it has happened. Why should you? You just want to make a call.

The soft radio in your device will work out for itself if that you have walked into a Wi-Fi zone and load Wi-Fi software to use that network. "The device will go into a halt state, unload one lot of communications software and load another, without interrupting you," says Longbottom.

You may not see the join, but your finance director will. Every time a call shifts to the office LAN, your company saves money. And every time your sales people get a call or a mail they might otherwise miss, your company makes money.

what device? who knows?

But what about all those devices? Something radical is going to happen to them. At the moment, every device tries to be a Swiss Army knife, and do the job of all the others. Phones do email, PDAs display spreadsheets, and laptops carry phone software. This is madness, says Longbottom.

All those devices can communicate with each other using short range radio (Bluetooth at the moment, and something much faster called UWB in future). If they can communicate with each other, why does each device insist on trying to do everything? You'd never accept that duplication of effort in a team of humans, so why stand for it in a team of devices?

If one device has the best radio, all the other devices should use it and save effort all round: "Use the short-range radio with the longest battery life to talk to the best radio," he says. That way, you can have "always on" connections without running your batteries down in a flash.

"In the long run, we will break apart the devices," says Longbottom. The PDA, the phone and laptop all have screens, and all have some means of getting information into them. In future, will just use the best screen and the best input method for each job, not the one that happens to be turned on at the time. Personal area networks (PANs) will make it possible.

Imagine the situation where you are checking email on a PDA, and come across an urgent message with a spreadsheet attachment. You need a big screen to view it, and a keyboard to work on it, so that means your laptop. At the moment, your only option is to put down the PDA, boot up the laptop, load email and hunt around through your in-tray to the same message.

In future, the PDA will spot there is a spreadsheet attachment. It knows you prefer to see that kind of file on a bigger screen and checks what's available in arm's reach. It finds your laptop, fires up the screen, and offers to display the file there, for you to work on. You just say yes, and away you go.

In fact, the data is probably already on your laptop, because the PDA is continually backing it up there. "A laptop could be your PAN's storage device, working quietly with the screen turned off," says Longbottom.

If you prefer to keep things on your phone when possible, the PAN will do its best to keep jobs there. If the laptop isn't available, it will remember the job, and remind you of it, when there's a decent screen available. The job will follow your preference, and the tools you need.

"Trying to get all the functions in one device is doomed to failure," says Longbottom. He concedes that there's scant sign of any vendor handing over its ambition to do everything just yet, but it is all so new that vendors are trying everything out. The tide of too-complex devices will eventually turn, he says.

batteries get better

Cutting down redundancy in your devices will do wonders, but the devices will still impinge on you when you need to charge the battery. That problem will go away eventually, as fuel cells – which make their own energy from methanol – are coming.

"Any improvement in battery technology is short term," says Longbottom. "We need to move to a technology that makes its own power."

Fuel cell technology has been practical for a while, but there have been fears about its safety. Now the UN's expert advisers have passed fuel cells to be carried on planes, so that worry is diminishing. The first consumer/business devices that use fuel cells will appear in 2005. In five years they will be widespread.

the downside

There are downsides, of course, and nothing will be perfect. But the technology will work round any problems, without bothering you.

"Always on" connections will still have dead spots, for instance, as you walk past a particular metal-framed building. But the connection will be buffered so you won't lose data. Fuel cells won't run for ever, but switching work to a new device or a new battery will be easier.

easy to use

Working with technology will be easier, because the technology will take pains to work with us. As devices become an extension of ourselves, the data in them will be easier to use and the links they make with other people will be more natural and easier to use than ever before.

The sign of success will be the fact that we are completely unaware of all this. We will be using all the technology available, without having to think about it.

glossary
(non-technophiles start here)

3G – stands for third generation technology

The first generation (1G) mobile network, which appeared in the 1980s, were analogue in nature and not that different in call quality terms from Citizen's Band radios. In the early 1990s, GSM – (2G) networks arrived, giving users access to mobile digital call quality, as well as mobile data for the first time. 3G's main claim to fame is even better call quality, as well as faster mobile Internet and video/email access.

advantages: clearer voice calls, faster downloads, videomail.

disadvantages: bulkier handsets, less rural coverage at present.

Bluetooth – personal area networking

A wireless personal area network with an effective range of 10 to 100 feet, Bluetooth was originally designed for voice communications, Unlike Wi-Fi, which was designed as a static wireless data technology. Despite overlap between the two technologies, Bluetooth is far cheaper to deploy and use than Wi-Fi. The technology uses lower power radio signals than Wi-Fi, making it ideal for use on mobile phones.

advantages: lower power outputs and costs than Wi-Fi. Seen on a growing number of mobile phones.

disadvantages: limited range; not designed for data – transmissions; lower power means more subject to local interference sources such as office/domestic microwaves etc.

GPRS – stands for General Packet Radio Service

GPRS supports mobile data speeds of around 30 to 40,000 kilobits per second by the simple expedient of daisy-chaining two or more GSM data channels together. Often referred to as 2.5G, GPRS operates at roughly the same speed as a dial-up landline modem Internet connection, but on a mobile basis.

advantages:	uses GSM network technology, ensuring maximum possible coverage with minimal GSM network modifications. GSM is in active use in 200-plus countries around the world.
disadvantages:	using multiple GSM data channels means the mobile phone or device uses more power than for voice calls. Uses more network resources than for voice calls, so can overload a local network at peak times.

Notebook

A notebook PC is a complete desktop PC system in a portable format. Subject to battery power issues, a notebook can replace a desktop, although prices of notebooks are typically twice that of a similar desktop PC. The latest notebook PCs come with an Intel Centrino chipset at their heart, which supports Wi-Fi (wireless LAN) technology without having to install an add-on card.

advantages:	wide range of desktop PC software available. Can replace a desktop PC for many users. Centrino users also get Wi-Fi facilities as standard.
disadvantages:	takes time to boot up; battery power measured at a few hours maximum. Even without an integral drive, the smallest notebooks are not what you would call 'pocketable'.

PDA – stands for personal digital assistant

A PDA is a half-way house between a smartphone and a notebook PC. First seen in the late 1980s, PDAs only came into their own in the mid-1990s as processor speeds and power issues were conquered. PDAs have larger and better screens than smartphones, as well as faster boot-up times than notebook PCs. PDAs are more software-driven than smartphones, with the result that many more applications are available for PDAs, although their downside is that they require PDA-specific versions of applications – ie. you can't load up the latest PC copy of MS-Word.

advantages:	larger screen, more flexible than smartphones.
disadvantages:	not as wide a choice of software as a notebook. Consumes more power than a smartphone.

Smartphone

A smartphone is an advanced mobile phone that includes a number of simple PDA functions, such as email, note-taking, scheduling etc., as standard. Today's smartphones often include a digital camera and extra communications facilities such as Wi-Fi and Bluetooth as standard.

advantages: a half-way house between a standard mobile phone and a PDA. Better mobile data interfacing than most low-end PDAs.

disadvantages: power can also be an issue with the latest colour-screen smartphones.

Wi-Fi – stands for Wireless LAN

Based on the 802.11 standard – and available in a, b, g and other upcoming flavours – Wi-Fi is a high-speed wireless network standard that is now supported by Intel's Centrino processor chipset. Notebooks with Centrino chipsets can use an accessible Wi-Fi network without requiring extra hardware. Public access Wi-Fi points now number into five figures in the UK and, although nowhere near the blanket coverage that 3G or GSM enjoys, Wi-Fi's key advantage – speed of access – is very useful in many city areas. The technology can also be used in office areas at relatively low cost.

advantages: low-cost, standards-driven technology. Easy to install and use.

disadvantages: requires users to be stationary. Finite (200 feet maximum) range.

resources

ConnectAnyWhere – mobile messaging supplier
www.connectanywhere.co.uk

Department of Trade and Industry Best Practice site
www.dti.gov.uk/bestpractice

Expansys – Communications supplier site with good links/resources
www.expansys.com

GSM World – site for international roamers
www.gsmworld.com

Institute of Directors
www.iod.com

Mobile Computer Users Group
www.mcug.org.uk

Mobileinfo – mobile computing and wireless site
www.mobileinfo.com

Mobile Shop – buyers' guides and advice
www.mobileshop.org

Mobile Interaction and Pervasive Social Devices – research network
http://mobility.is.lse.ac.uk

Ofcom
www.ofcom.org.uk

Silicon – business and technology news
www.silicon.com

Smartphone.net – smartphone resource
www.smartphone.net

Telecoms Advice
www.telecomsadvice.org.uk

The Complete Guide to Flexible Working
www.flexibility.co.uk/guide

Vodafone – mobile network operator and sponsor of this guide
www.vodafone.co.uk

www.telappliant.com – UK Internet telephone specialist with good resources

www.wifi411.com – search Wi-Fi hot spots (both free and pay) globally

www.wigle.net – second Wi-Fi search resource

www.wi-fiplanet.com – everything Wi-Fi

Wi-Fi Alliance – non-profit association
www.wi-fi.org

Wireless Ecademy – wireless and mobility resource
http://wireless.ecademy.com

Wireless World Forum
www.w2forum.com

Vodafone UK

Vodafone UK has 14.6 million customers and is part of the world's largest mobile community. The Newbury-based company offers a wide range of mobile voice and data communications. The Vodafone UK network covers 99 per cent of the population and transmits over 17.5 million text messages every day. Vodafone UK was the world's first mobile operator to introduce international roaming, and currently offers its customers roaming on 408 networks in 174 countries.

The Vodafone Business Enterprise Unit is a dedicated unit within Vodafone UK, created to understand and satisfy the communications needs of all companies, from small business start-ups to multinational corporations. Its focus is to deliver value-added voice and data services that improve productivity, integrate with existing IT infrastructures and solve specific business problems.

In May 2004, Vodafone UK was ranked top for customer satisfaction in the UK's contract mobile phone sector in a survey by JD Power and Associates.

www.vodafone.co.uk